Number Skills

Miles Kelly

About the consultant

Experienced Key Stage 1 and Key Stage 2 teacher Caroline Clissold is passionate about raising standards in mathematics teaching in primary schools. She was a consultant and regional co-ordinator for the National Centre for Excellence in the Teaching of Mathematics, delivers in-service training for a specialist mathematics education publisher, supports teaching and learning in various schools, and has guest lectured at a number of London universities. Her aim is to increase children's enjoyment of mathematics, helping them to see purpose in their learning. She strongly believes in a creative approach to teaching so that children can use and apply maths skills in meaningful contexts.

First published in 2020 by Miles Kelly Publishing Ltd
Harding's Barn, Bardfield End Green, Thaxted, Essex, CM6 3PX, UK

Copyright © Miles Kelly Publishing Ltd 2020

2 4 6 8 10 9 7 5 3 1

Publishing Director Belinda Gallagher
Creative Director Jo Cowan
Editorial Director Rosie Neave
Managing Designer Joe Jones
Designer Venita Kidwai
Illustrators Clare Fennell, Laura Watson
Production Elizabeth Collins, Jennifer Brunwin-Jones
Image Manager Liberty Newton
Reprographics Stephan Davis
Assets Lorraine King

ISBN 978-1-78989-101-0

Printed in China

British Library Cataloguing-in-Publication Data
A catalogue record for this book is available from the British Library

Made with paper from a sustainable forest

CONTENTS

Equals 4 - 47

Addition and Subtraction 48–95

1 1 1 1 1 1 1

2 2 2

3 3 3

4 4 4

5 5 5

6 6 6

7 7 7

8 8 8

9 9 9

10 10 10

4

Equals

...with The Gingerbread Man!

Draw along the dotted lines.

EQUALS

Making things equal

Equals means the same as or equivalent to. Your child needs to develop an understanding of the word equal and its symbol: =

Once they have explored numbers from one to ten, children learn to compare them and make them equal. They compare by finding numbers that are smaller or greater than the number they have. Finding more means adding, and finding less means subtracting. Once your child has explored the concepts of more and less, they will progress to identifying when two numbers are equal.

- Sometimes children develop a misconception that after the equals symbol comes the answer to a calculation. The symbol means that whatever is on one side must be the same as or equal to what is on the other.

- Balancing toy blocks or similar objects on old-fashioned weighing scales can help your child gain a conceptual understanding of the word equal.

- If your child can recognize numerals, it's good practice to show them a numeral written down and ask them to find or show you that number of objects.

INSTRUCTION TEXT explains what your child will learn on each spread and how to approach the activities. Key words are shown in *italics*

STORY TEXT keeps your child engaged and makes learning and practising fun

ILLUSTRATIONS contain clues to help your child complete the activities. Look for the clues together and encourage your child to count out loud as they point.

ACTIVITIES guide your child through the stages of learning about the concept of equals

Compare: Mo

Your child will compare numbers to decide which more and which is *less*. Help them c the items and write the numbers in the Then help your child to draw the co symbols in the circles.
> means *more than*
< means *less than*

How many **flowers** are in each group? Which group has m

3

22

Eq

Cross

Tick

32

NUMBER TRACK
can be used to help your child decide whether one number is more or less than another. If they have to move their finger left on the track from the first number to the second, then the first number is more. If they have to move their finger right it is less. It's good practice for your child to trace the numerals, too.

CHARACTER SPEECH
provides extra activities, tips and guidance

Can you see more ducks, or more clouds?

...hey were halfway
...the fox said, "The
...is getting deep.
...onto my head." So
...gerbread man did.

...many **tadpoles**
...each group?
...group has more?

How many **frogs** are in each group? Which group has more?

How many **dragonflies** are in each group? Which group has more?

6 ◯ 3 ◯ 5 ◯ 2

to page 42

Well done! 23

SQUARE BOXES
are for numbers;
ROUND BOXES
are for symbols

DOTTED LINES
to trace throughout help to improve pen control

TICKS
for your child to trace when they complete each spread provide an extra sense of achievement

...ns **balance**

...th an **unequal** number of things.
...h an **equal** number of things.

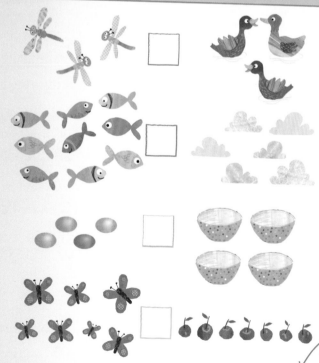

Well done! 33

Find one more

To find one *more* than a number, ask your child to put their finger on that number on the number track, then lift their finger and place it on the number to the right. Finding one more is the same as *adding* one. Help your child to write the numbers in the boxes.

One day a woman made a gingerbread man. She gave him currants for eyes and chocolate drops for buttons.

Find **one more** spoon.

How many are there now?

4 → 5

Find **one more** blueberry.

How many are there now?

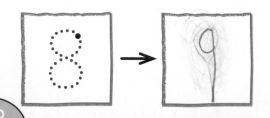

8 → 9

Find **one more** bowl.

How many are there now?

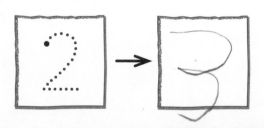

2 → 3

Draw **one more** eye.

How many are there now?

1 + 1 =

[ ] + 1 = 2

Can you follow the dotted lines on me to add more icing?

Draw **one more** button.

How many are there now?

3 + 1 =

[ ] + 1 = 4

For more practice turn to page 28

Well done!

9

Find one less

To find one *less* than a number, ask your child to put their finger on that number on the track, then lift their finger and place it on the number to the left. They can also cover up or cross out one of each type of item in the pictures and count how many are left. Finding one less is the same as *subtracting* one.

But when it was time to take the gingerbread man out of the oven, he ran away, crying, "Run, run, as fast as you can. You can't catch me, I'm the gingerbread man."

Someone eats

one sweet.

How many are left?

3 − 1 =

☐ − 1 = 2

Someone takes one nut.

How many are left?

9 − 1 =

☐ ☐ − 1 = 8

Cross **one** item out. How many are left?

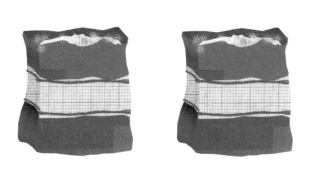

Find **one** less.

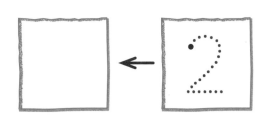

Find **one** less.

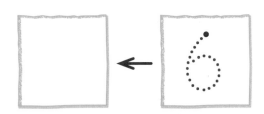

Find **one** less.

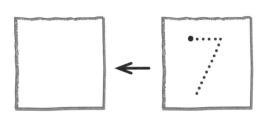

Find **one** less.

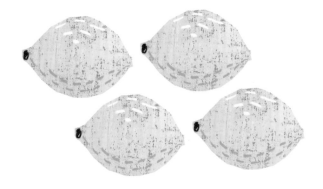

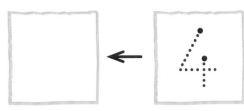

For more practice turn to page 30

Well done!

11

Equal means balance

Help your child to identify whether numbers on each side of the scales below are *equal* or *unequal*. The word *equal* means *the same as* or *equivalent to*. Continue to use the words *more* and *less*.

"Stop him!" yelled the woman to her husband. But the gingerbread man hopped just out of reach.

Cross the balances that are **unequal**.

Tick the balances that are **equal**.

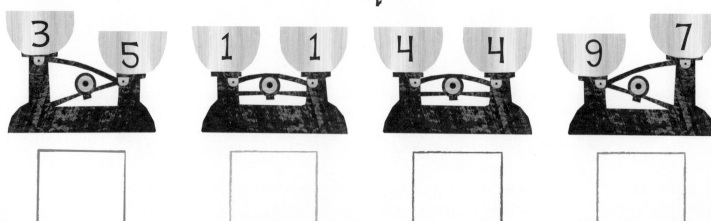

1 2 3 4 5 6 7 8 9 10

As he did so, he cried, "Run, run as fast as you can. You can't catch me, I'm the gingerbread man."

Does the man's shirt have more buttons than me?

For more practice turn to page 32

Well done!

13

Equals: Addition

The gingerbread man ran out of the kitchen. "Stop him!" yelled the man to the cat. The cat ran after the gingerbread man too.

$$5 + \boxed{} = 6$$

$$4 = 1 + \boxed{}$$

But the gingerbread man said, "Run, run, as fast as you can. You can't catch me, I'm the gingerbread man."

$8 = \boxed{} + 7$

How many more birds do you have to draw to equal the number of bees?

$6 + 1 = \boxed{}$

For more practice turn to page 34

Well done!

15

Equals: Subtraction

In this activity your child will use subtraction to make an equal number statement. Cover up or cross out one of each type of item in the pictures and count how many are left. Help your child to write the correct numbers in the boxes. Check each calculation with them on the number track.

"Stop him!" yelled the cat to the dog. So the dog joined the chase too.

$$5 - \boxed{} = 4$$

$$6 - 1 = \boxed{}$$

Trace my stripes and count them. Is the number less than the number of sheep?

1 2 3 4 5 6 7 8 9 10

3 = 4 − ☐

But the gingerbread man said, "Run, run, as fast as you can. You can't catch me, I'm the gingerbread man."

8 = ☐ − 1

For more practice turn to page 36

Well done!

17

Equals: Addition and subtraction

The gingerbread man ran and ran until he reached the river. "I can't cross that!" he said.

$5 - 1 = \boxed{}$

$3 = 4 - \boxed{}$

18

A clever fox heard him and said, "Climb on my back – I can swim you across."

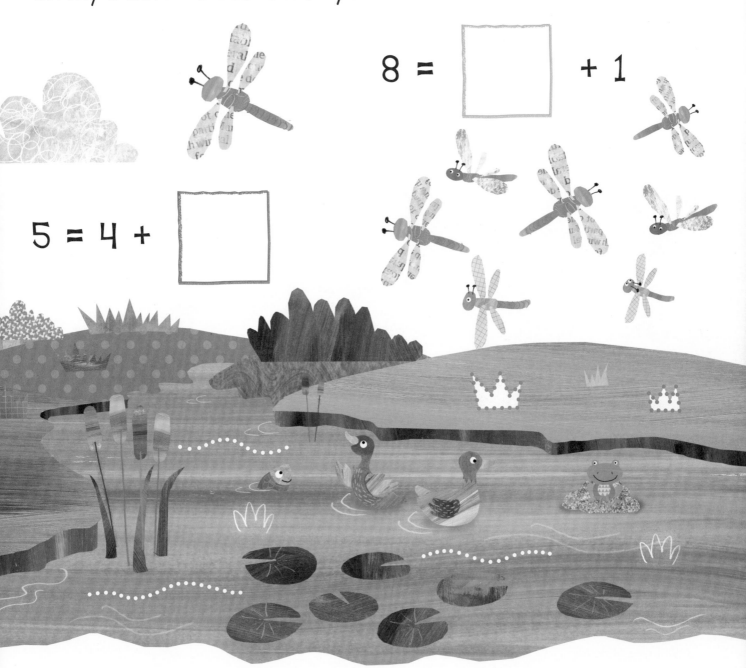

$8 = \boxed{} + 1$

$5 = 4 + \boxed{}$

$7 - \boxed{} = 6$

For more practice turn to page 38

Well done!

19

More or less?

So the gingerbread man climbed onto the fox's back.

As the fox began to swim, he said, "Climb up to my neck so you don't get wet." So the gingerbread man did.

Draw the stalks for the bulrushes. How many can you see?

20

Write the correct numbers in the boxes.

Draw **one** more.

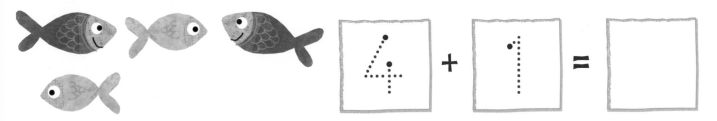

$$4 + 1 = \boxed{}$$

Draw **one** more.

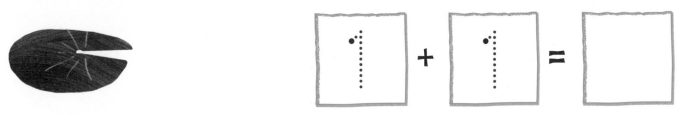

$$1 + 1 = \boxed{}$$

Find **one** less.

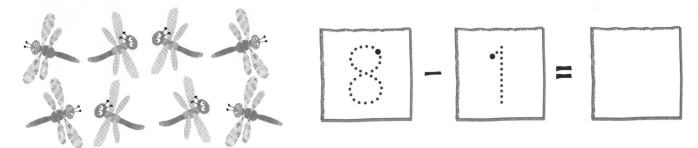

$$8 - 1 = \boxed{}$$

Find **one** less.

$$3 - 1 = \boxed{}$$

For more practice turn to page 40

Well done!

Compare: More or less?

When they were halfway across, the fox said, "The water is getting deep. Climb onto my head." So the gingerbread man did.

How many **flowers** are in each group?

Which group has more?

How many **tadpoles** are in each group?

Which group has more?

 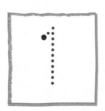   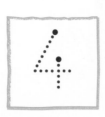  

How many **frogs** are in each group?

Which group has more?

How many **dragonflies** are in each group?

Which group has more?

For more practice turn to page 42

Well done!

23

Compare: More, less or equal?

When they were nearly across, the fox said, "Climb onto my nose. Then I know you'll be safe." So the gingerbread man did.

Add one more stripe to each fish.

24

How many **lily pads** are in each group?

Fill the circle with the correct symbol.

How many **fish** are in each group?

Fill the circle with the correct symbol.

How many **bubbles** are in each group?

Fill the circle with the correct symbol.

For more practice
turn to page 44

Well done!

25

More numbers to compare

Like the activity on the previous page, here your child is comparing numbers to decide if one is *more* and one is *less*, or if they are *equal*.

But then the fox threw his head up, and the gingerbread man flew up in the air.

How many **rocks** are in each group?

Fill the circle with the correct symbol.

How many **bulrushes** are in each group?

Fill the circle with the correct symbol.

How many **birds** are in each group?

Fill the circle with the correct symbol.

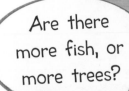

Are there more fish, or more trees?

1 2 3 4 5 6 7 8 9 10

The fox opened his mouth, and with one SNAP!
– the gingerbread man was gone.

"Delicious!" said the fox.

For more practice turn to page 46

Well done!

Find one more

Find **one more** lemon.

How many are there now?

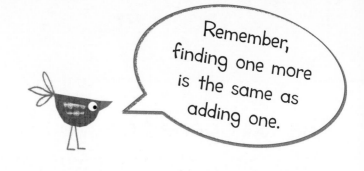

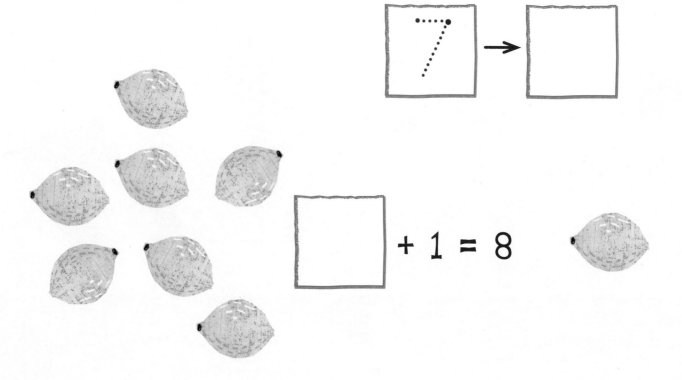

+ 1 = 8

Find **one more** raspberry.

How many are there now?

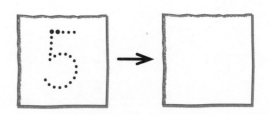

5 + 1 =

1 2 3 4 5 6 7 8 9 10

Find **one more** egg.

How many are there now?

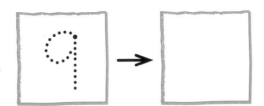

Use the
number track
to help you.

9 + 1 =

Find **one more** bag of flour.

How many are there now?

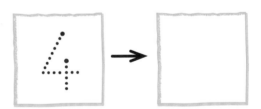

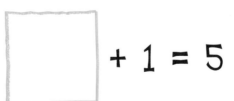 + 1 = 5

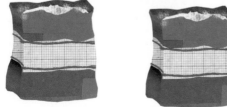

Well done!

29

Find one less

Cross **one** item out. How many are left?

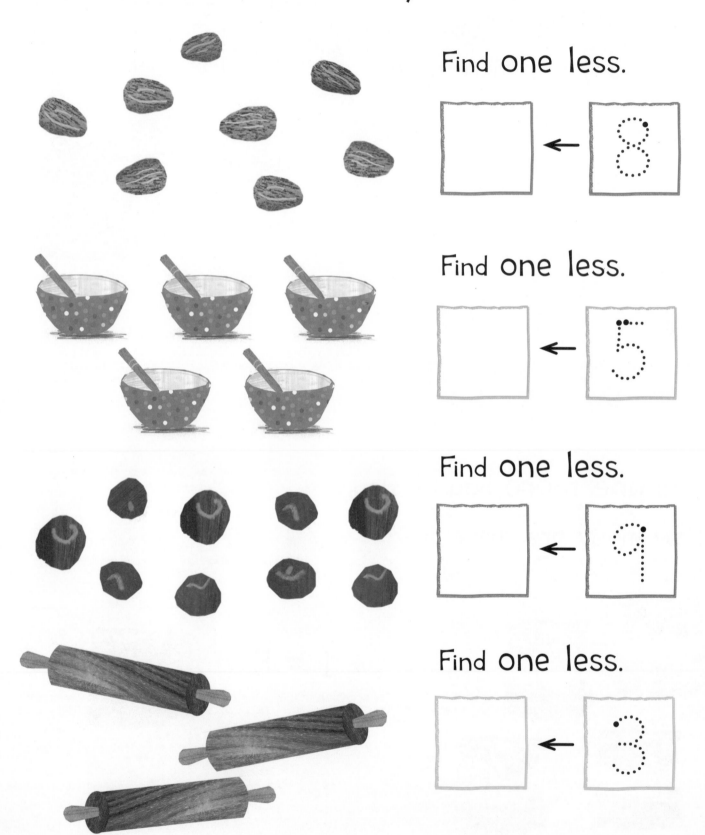

Find **one** less.

☐ ← 8

Find **one** less.

☐ ← 5

Find **one** less.

☐ ← 9

Find **one** less.

☐ ← 3

1 2 3 4 5 6 7 8 9 10

Find one less.

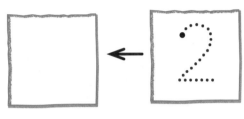

Find one less.

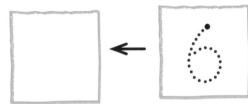

Find one less.

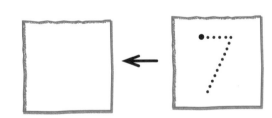

Find one less.

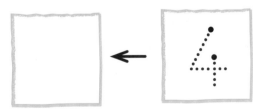

Well done!

Equal means balance

Cross the groups with an **unequal** number of things.

Tick the groups with an **equal** number of things.

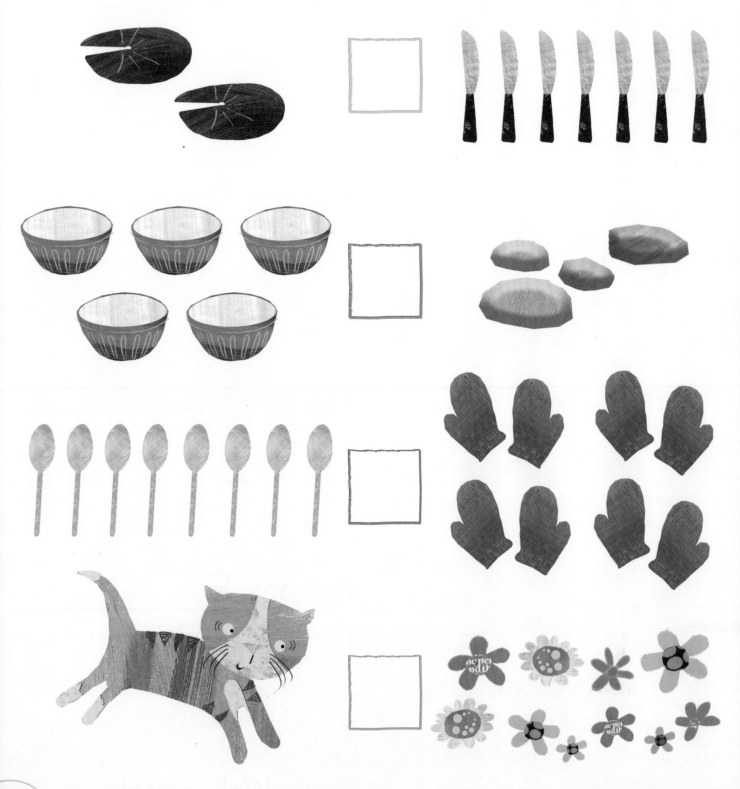

1 2 3 4 5 6 7 8 9 10

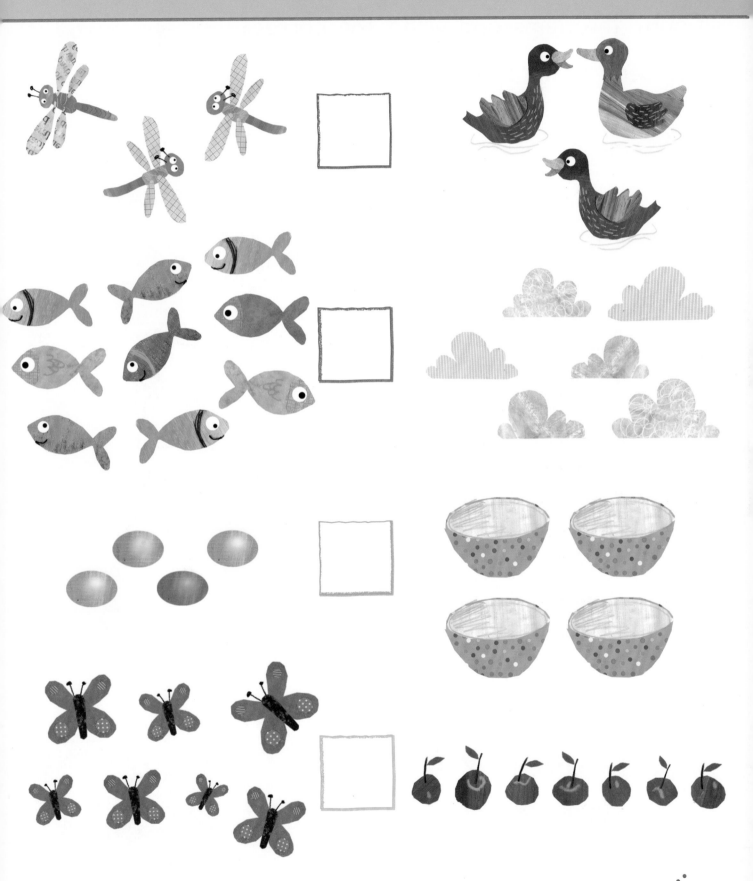

Well done!

Equals: Addition

Count the items and write the correct numbers in the boxes.

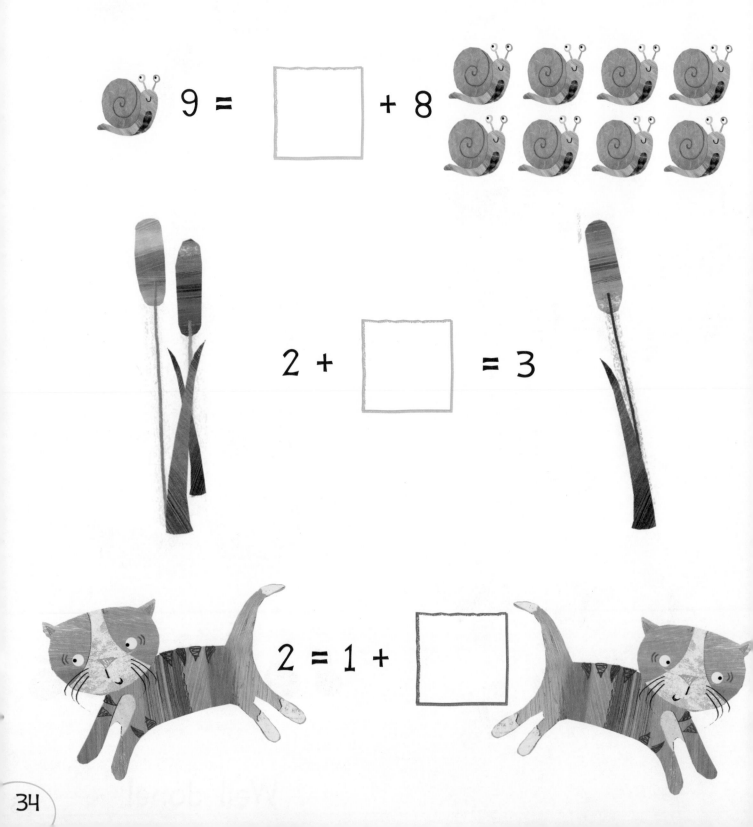

9 = ☐ + 8

2 + ☐ = 3

2 = 1 + ☐

34

1 2 3 4 5 6 7 8 9 10

Use the number track to check your calculations.

6 + ☐ = 7

4 = 3 + ☐

5 = ☐ + 4

Well done!

Equals: Subtraction

Cross out one of each type of item in the pictures. Count the remaining items and write the correct numbers in the boxes.

$2 = 3 - \boxed{}$

$7 - \boxed{} = 6$

$4 - 1 = \boxed{}$

Use the number track to check your calculations.

7 = ☐ − 1

4 = 5 − ☐

6 − ☐ = 5

Well done!

Equals: Addition and subtraction

Make these number statements equal by writing the correct numbers in the boxes.

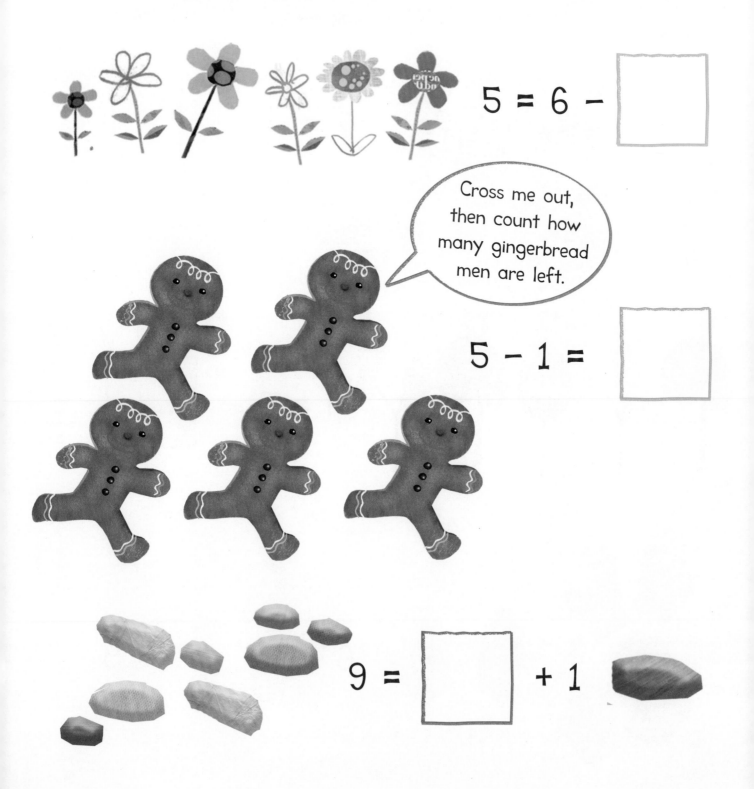

$5 = 6 - \boxed{}$

Cross me out, then count how many gingerbread men are left.

$5 - 1 = \boxed{}$

$9 = \boxed{} + 1$

Use the number track to check your calculations.

7 = ☐ + 1

2 = 1 + ☐

8 − ☐ = 7

Well done!

More or less?

Write the correct numbers in the boxes.

Draw **one** more.

$3 + 1 = \boxed{}$

Draw **one** more.

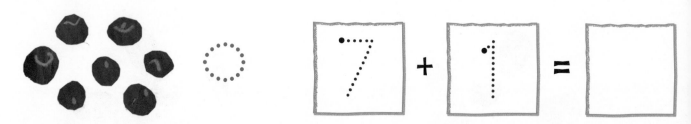

$7 + 1 = \boxed{}$

Draw **one** more.

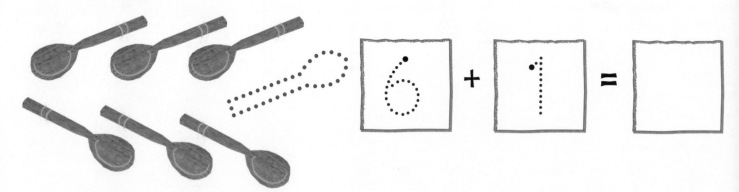

$6 + 1 = \boxed{}$

Draw **one** more.

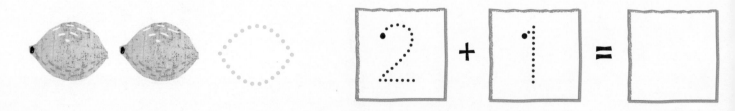

$2 + 1 = \boxed{}$

Find **one** less.

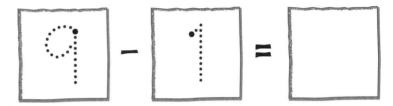

$$9 - 1 = \boxed{}$$

Find **one** less.

Cross me out, then count the ducks that are left.

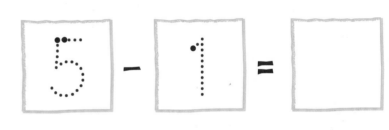

$$5 - 1 = \boxed{}$$

Find **one** less.

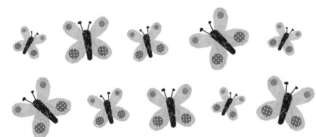

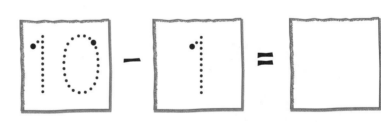

$$10 - 1 = \boxed{}$$

Find **one** less.

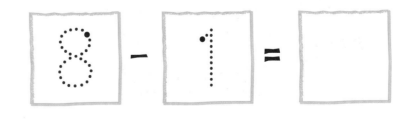

$$8 - 1 = \boxed{}$$

Well done!

41

Compare: More or less?

How many are in each group? Which group has more?
Write the correct symbol in each circle.

Well done!

43

Compare: More, less or equal?

How many are in each group? Write the correct symbol in each circle.

> means more than
< means less than
= means equal

1 2 3 4 5 6 7 8 9 10

Well done!

45

More numbers to compare

How many are in each group? Write the correct symbol in each circle.

> means more than
< means less than
= means equal

1 2 3 4 5 6 7 8 9 10

Well done!

47

1

2

3

4

5

6

7

8

9

10

Let's start practising!

48

Addition and Subtraction

Adding and subtracting

As children learn to add and subtract, they start to see the relationship between the two. They begin to understand that addition is commutative (the order you add doesn't matter – the answer is always the same) and subtraction is not. They will also begin to see that addition and subtraction are inverse (opposite) operations.

There are two models (systems) of *addition* that young children need to be aware of:

Augmentation is when you have an amount and add another amount to it. For example: Amy had six marbles, Fran gave her two more – how many does Amy have now?
Aggregation is the coming together of two amounts. For example: Nik baked four cakes and Sam baked three. How many did they bake altogether?

There are two models of *subtraction* that young children need to be aware of:

Take away is when an amount is taken away from the whole. For example, Ben had eight sweets and ate two – how many were left?
Difference is how many more or less an amount is compared with another. For example: Tom had five teddies, Polly had two. How many more did Tom have?

NUMBER PAIRS

Young children need to learn the number pairs (or number bonds) to 10. A number pair is two numbers that add up to another number. Memorizing number pairs to 10, then 20 and after that 100 are helpful for several reasons, including mental calculation.

STORY TEXT
keeps your child engaged and makes learning and practising fun

INSTRUCTION TEXT
explains what your child will be learning on each spread and how to approach the activities

NUMBER ACTIVITIES
guide your child through the process of learning to add and subtract, step by step. It may be helpful to also let your child use practical objects as you work through the pages

66

Adding 1 and adding 2

Jack's mum had four apples. Jack picked one more
How many apples are there now?

$$4 + 1 =$$

Seven bugs are joined by two more.
How many bugs are there now?

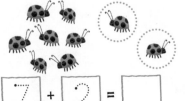

$$7 + 2 =$$

72

cts for 8

Then the giant put a gold harp onto the table. "Play!" he growled. It played so sweetly that the giant was soon asleep. Jack crept out of the pot.

☐ + ☐ = 8

8

☐   ☐

Draw around each group of items that shows a way to make eight.

8 - ☐ = ☐

turn to page 86   Well done!   67

NUMBER TRACK highlights the number or numbers that the pages are focusing on. It's good practice for your child to trace the numerals, too

ILLUSTRATIONS contain clues to help your child complete the activities. Look for the clues together and encourage your child to count out loud as they point

CHARACTER SPEECH provides extra activities, tips and guidance

TICKS for your child to trace when they complete each spread provide an extra sense of achievement

1 2 3 4 5 6 7 8 9 10

There are three white ducks and one grey duck.

How many ducks are there **altogether**?

3 + 1 = ☐   3   1

There are six gold coins and two silver coins.

How many coins are there **altogether**?

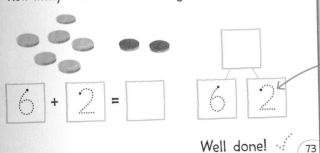

6 + 2 = ☐   6   2

Well done!   73

DOTTED LINES to trace throughout help to improve pen control

51

Adding 1 and adding 2

These activities explore the two models for addition. Help your child to write the correct numbers in the boxes.

Jack and his mum were so poor that they decided to sell their only cow. On the way to market Jack met a man who offered him two magic beans for his cow. Jack asked for one more bean – then he agreed.

How many beans are there **now**?

2 + 1 =

2

1

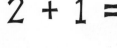

Jack ran home to tell his mum. On the way he saw some very strange things – magic was in the air.

To find out how many of us there are, add the number of chickens to the number of ducks.

How many birds are there **altogether?**

$5 + 2 =$

For more practice turn to page 72

Well done!

Subtracting 1 and subtracting 2

These activities explore the two models for subtraction (difference and comparison). Help your child to write the correct numbers in the boxes.

When Jack got home his mum was so cross she threw one bean out of the window! She put the others on the table and sent Jack to bed.

To find out how many beans there are now, subtract the number of beans thrown out of the window from the number Jack had before.

How many beans are there now?

3 – 1 = ☐

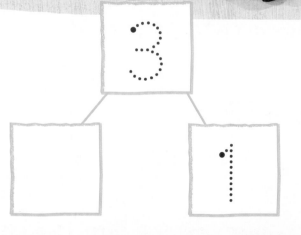

3

☐   1

The next morning, a huge beanstalk was growing outside Jack's window. It reached up into the clouds. "I told you they were magic beans," Jack said to his mum. He began to climb.

What is the **difference** between the number of bees and ladybirds?

4 − 2 =

4

2

For more practice turn to page 74

Well done!

Adding and subtracting 3

At the top Jack reached a castle. He knocked once on the door. No one answered. He knocked three more times and a giant woman opened it. "My husband eats boys for breakfast," she said.

How many times has Jack knocked on the door **now?**

$1 + 3 =$

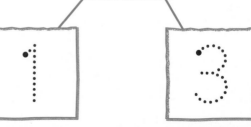

Three birds fly away. How many birds are there **now?**

6 − 3 = [ ]

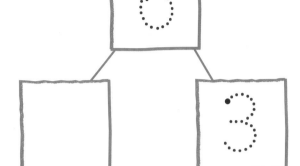

There are 7 flowers. 3 are yellow, the rest are red. How many red flowers are there?

7 − 3 = [ ]

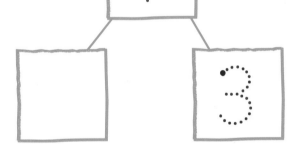

Jack and the woman both have patches on their clothes. How many are there **altogether?**

3 + 2 = [ ]

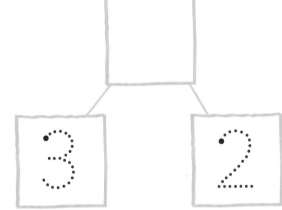

For more practice turn to page 76

Well done!

57

Number facts for 4

Help your child to write a correct number pair in the boxes on this page. They can use this number pair to complete the addition and subtraction number facts on the opposite page.

Then the ground began to shake. Jack ran into the kitchen and hid in a cupboard. A giant man stamped into the room. "Fee fi fo fum! I smell the blood of an Englishman!" he growled to his wife.

Draw around each group of items that shows a way to make four.

How can we make **four**?

"Don't be silly, dear," said the giant's wife.

$$\boxed{} + \boxed{} = 4$$

$$4 - \boxed{} = \boxed{}$$

For more practice turn to page 78

Well done!

Number facts for 5

The giant put a bag of gold coins on the table and then went to bed. Jack crept out of the cupboard and grabbed the bag.

Draw around each group of items that shows a way to make five.

How can we make **five**?

5

Jack rushed out of the castle and back down the beanstalk. His mum used some of the coins to buy five new cows.

☐ + ☐ = 5

5 - ☐ = ☐

For more practice turn to page 80

Well done!

61

Number facts for 6

Help your child to write a correct number pair in the boxes on this page. They can use this number pair to complete the addition and subtraction number facts on the opposite page.

A few weeks later, Jack decided to climb the beanstalk again. The giant's wife was not pleased to see him. "We lost a bag of gold the last time you were here," she growled. Then the ground began to shake.

Draw around each group of items that shows a way to make six.

How can we make six?

☐ + ☐ = 6

6 - ☐ = ☐

For more practice turn to page 82

Well done!

63

Number facts for 7

Jack dashed into the kitchen and hid in a cooking pot, just as the giant man stamped into the kitchen. "Fee fi fo fum! I smell the blood of an Englishman!" he roared.

How can we make **seven**?

"Look in the cupboard," said the giant's wife, but Jack wasn't there.

☐ + ☐ = 7

7 − ☐ = ☐

Draw around each group of items that shows a way to make seven.

For more practice turn to page 84

Well done!

Number facts for 8

Then the giant put a gold harp onto the table. "Play!" he growled. It played so sweetly that the giant was soon asleep. Jack crept out of the pot.

How can we make **eight?**

1 2 3 4 5 6 7 8 9 10

☐ + ☐ = 8

Draw around each group of items that shows a way to make eight.

8 − ☐ = ☐

For more practice turn to page 86 Well done!

Number facts for 9

Jack grabbed the harp and ran – but as soon as he touched it, the lovely music stopped.

How can we make **nine?**

The giant woke up at once and chased after Jack. Jack climbed down the beanstalk as fast he could, carrying the harp under his arm.

☐ + ☐ = 9

Draw around each group of items that shows a way to make nine.

9 – ☐ = ☐

For more practice turn to page 88

Well done!

Number facts for 10

As soon as Jack reached the ground he called to his mother to bring the axe. As fast as he could, Jack chopped through the beanstalk. Down it tumbled, and that was the end of the giant!

How can we make ten?

Jack and his mother lived happily for the rest of their days – with a whole herd of cows, and the lovely music of the golden harp.

☐ + ☐ = 10

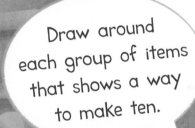

Draw around each group of items that shows a way to make ten.

10 − ☐ = ☐

For more practice turn to page 92

Well done!

71

Adding 1 and adding 2

Jack's mum had four apples. Jack picked one more.

How many apples are there **now**?

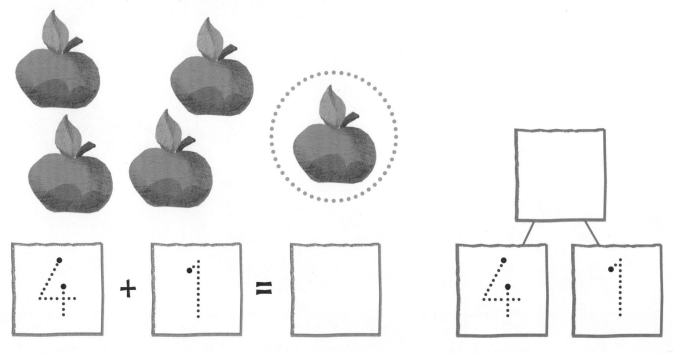

Seven bugs are joined by two more.

How many bugs are there **now**?

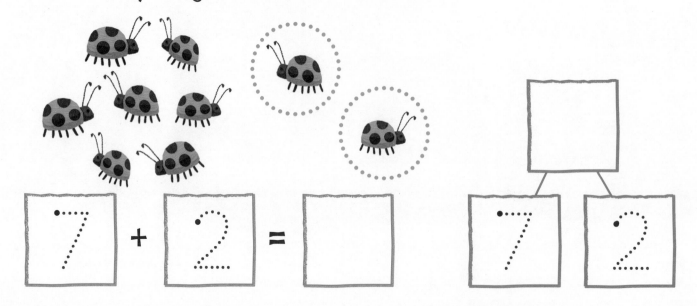

There are three white ducks and one grey duck.

How many ducks are there **altogether**?

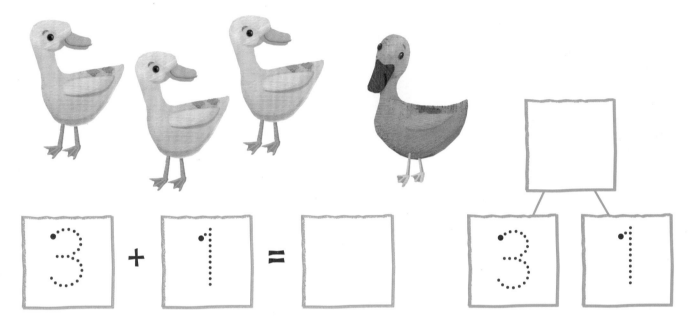

$$3 + 1 = \boxed{}$$

3 1

There are si**x** gold coins and two silver coins.

How many coins are there **altogether**?

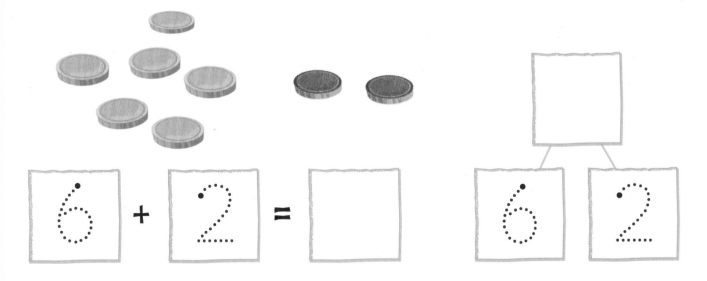

$$6 + 2 = \boxed{}$$

6 2

Well done!

Subtracting 1 and subtracting 2

Cross out one basket. How many are there **now**?

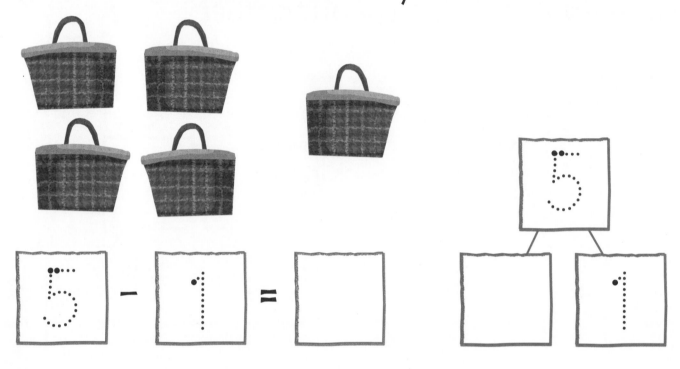

Cross out two oranges. How many are there **now**?

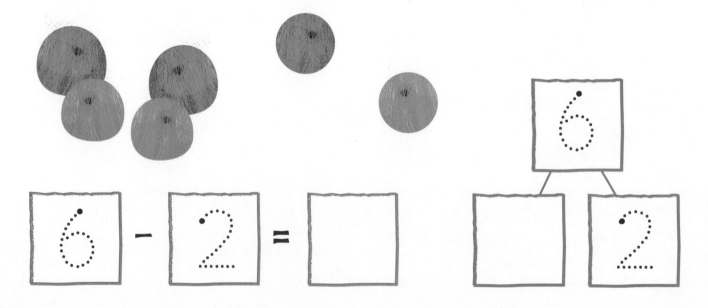

How many **more** cows with grey spots than cows with black spots are there?

$$3 - 2 = \boxed{} \qquad 3 \rightarrow \boxed{} \; 2$$

How many **more** green bottles than orange bottles are there?

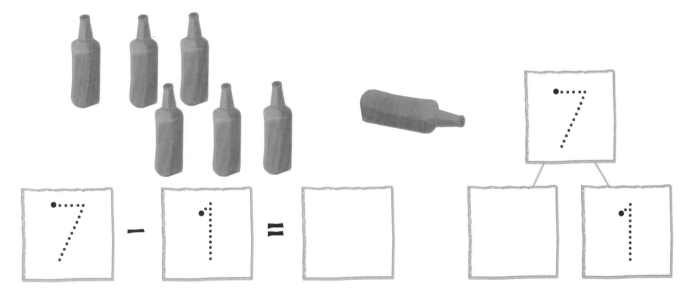

$$7 - 1 = \boxed{} \qquad 7 \rightarrow \boxed{} \; 1$$

Well done!

Adding and subtracting 3

Four bees are joined by three more.

How many are there **now**?

There are five blue clouds and three purple

clouds. How many are there **altogether?**

Cross out three leaves. How many are there **now**?

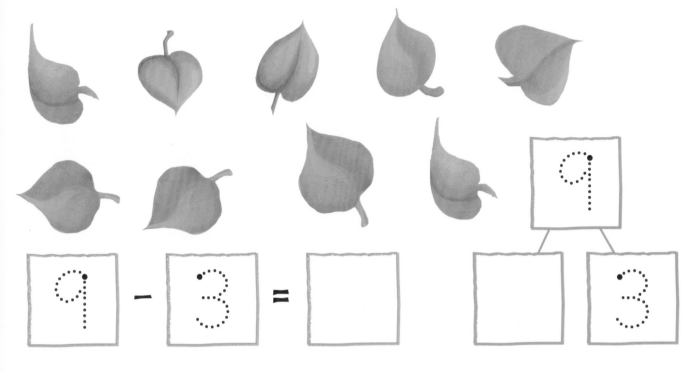

9 − 3 = [ ]

9
[ ] 3

How many **more** red roses than yellow roses are there?

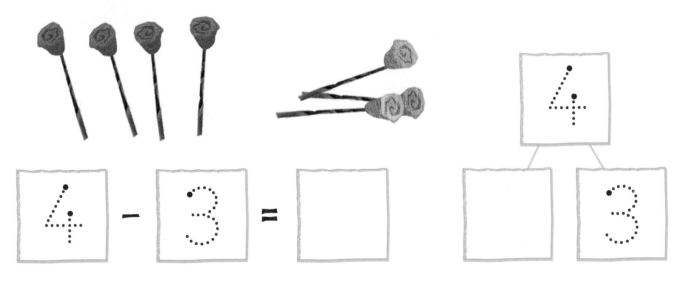

4 − 3 = [ ]

4
[ ] 3

Well done!

Number facts for 4

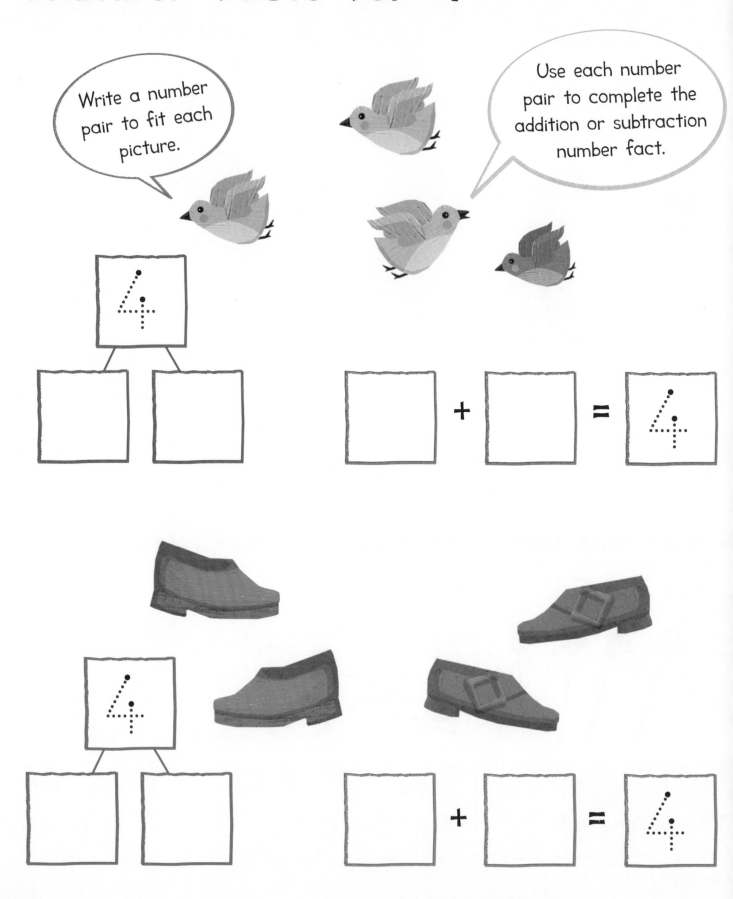

Write a number pair to fit each picture.

Use each number pair to complete the addition or subtraction number fact.

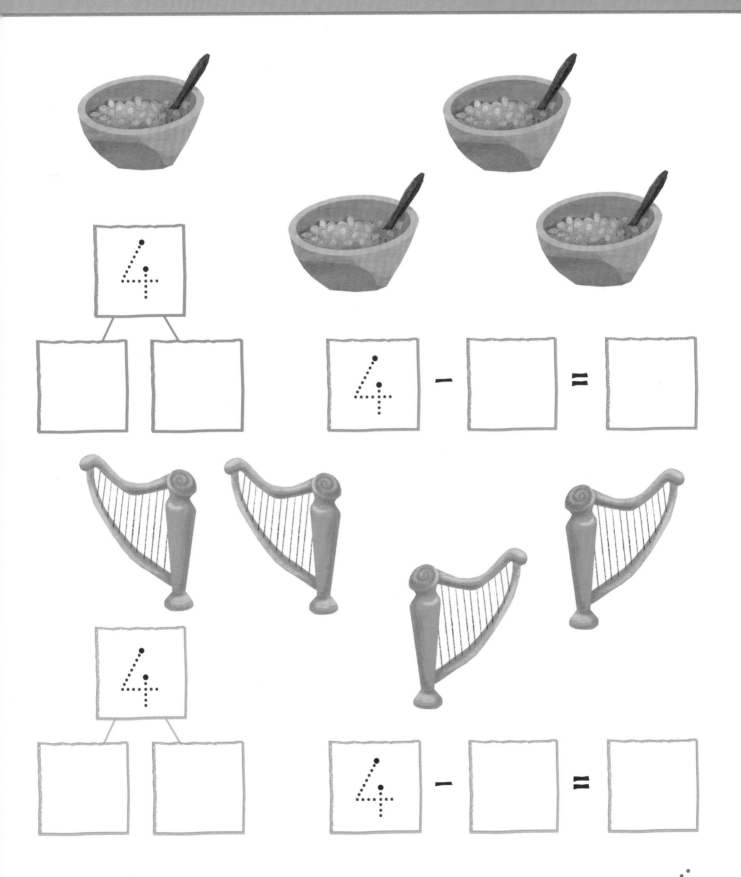

Well done!

Number facts for 5

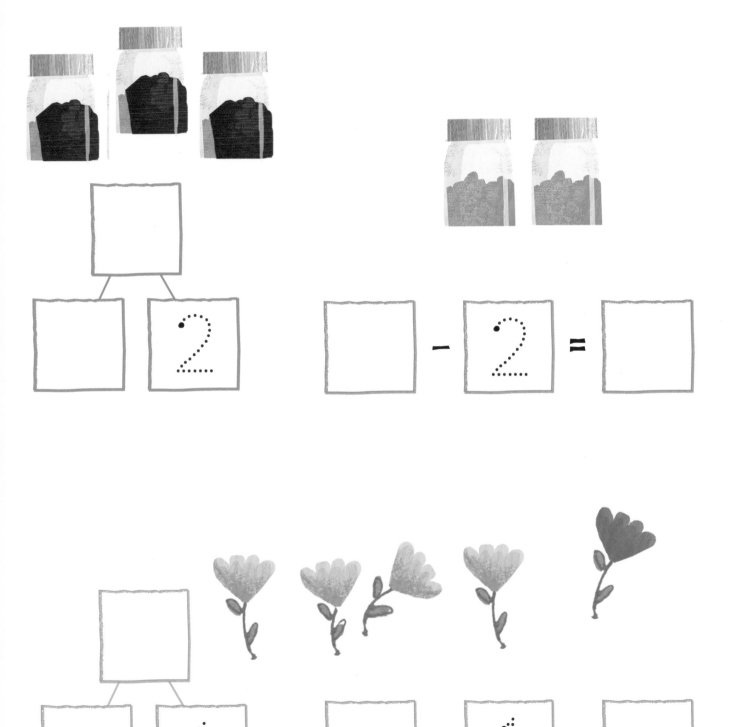

Well done!

Number facts for 6

Write a number pair to fit each picture.

Use each number pair to complete the addition or subtraction number fact.

82

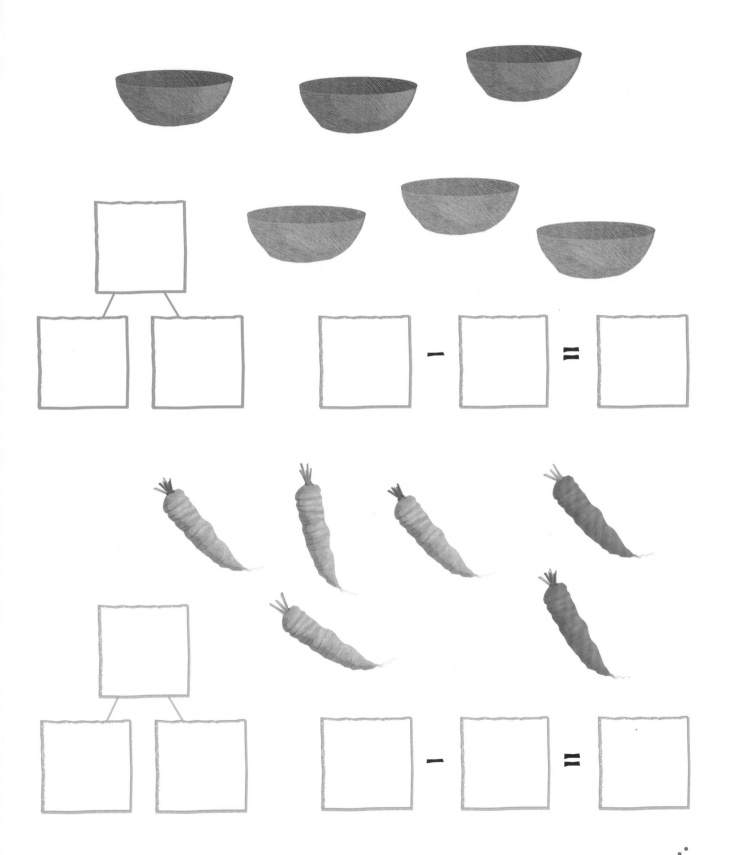

Well done!

Number facts for 7

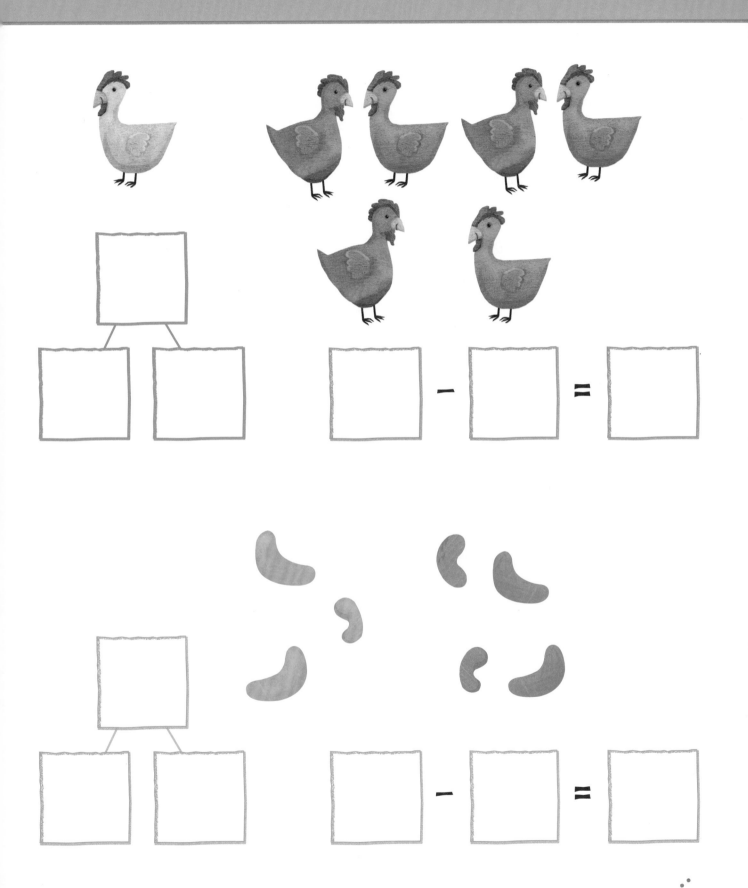

Well done!

Number facts for 8

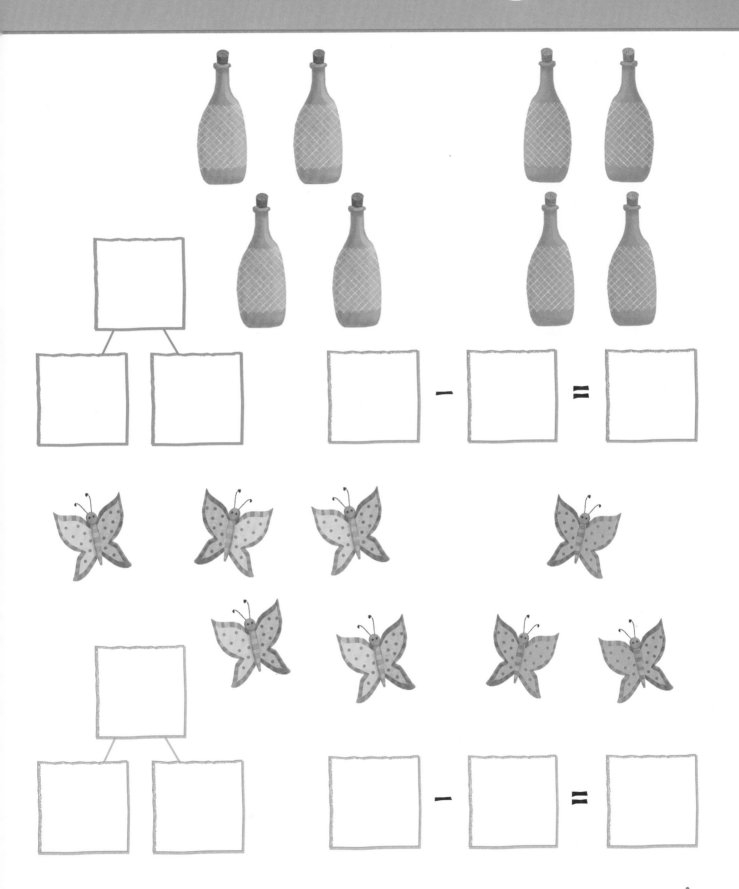

Well done!

87

Number facts for 9

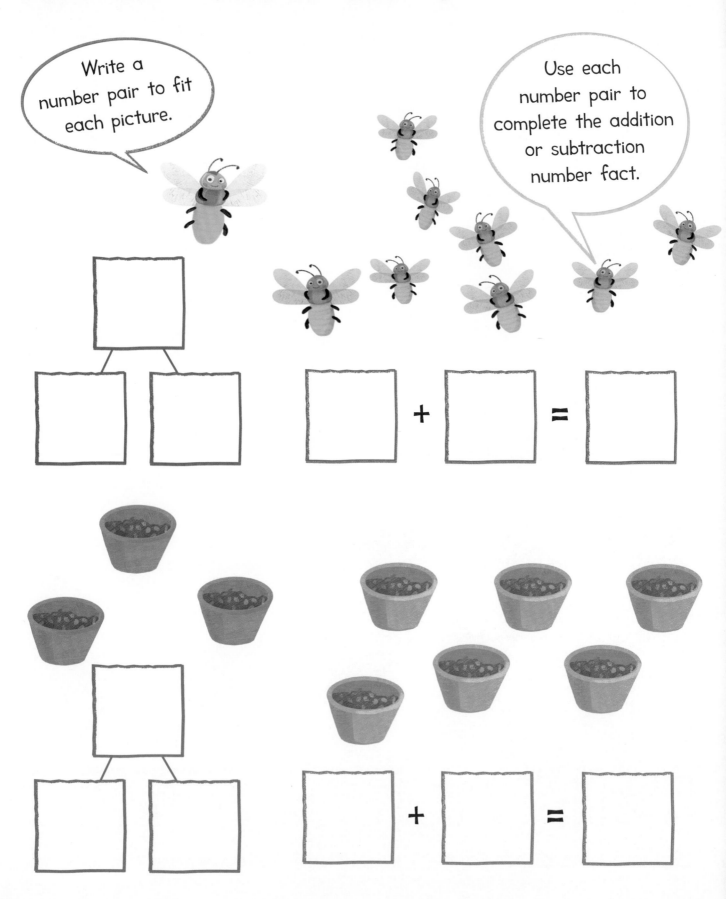

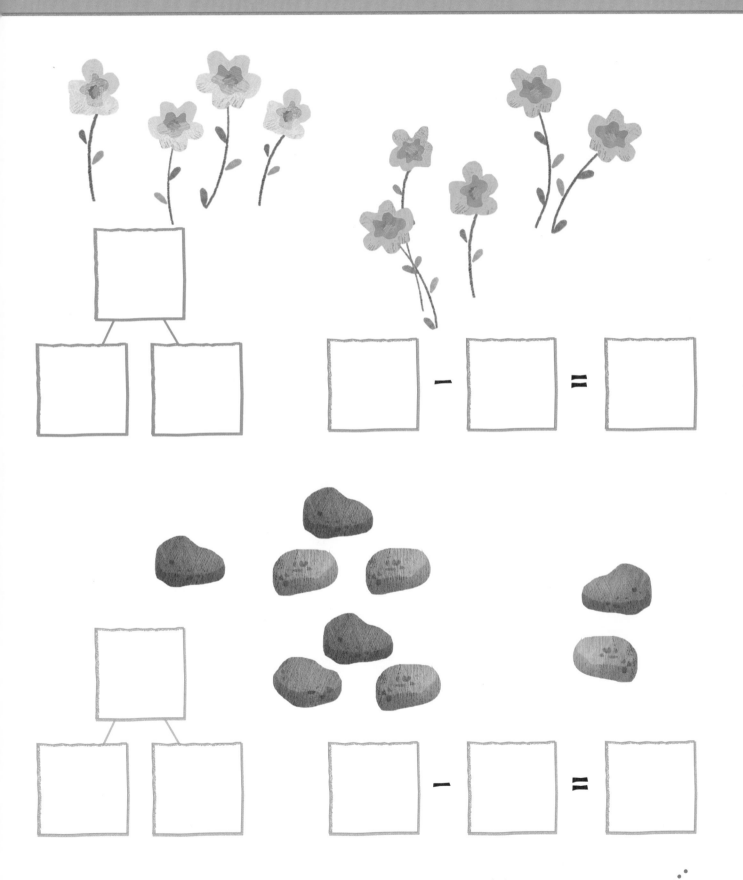

Well done!

More number facts for 9

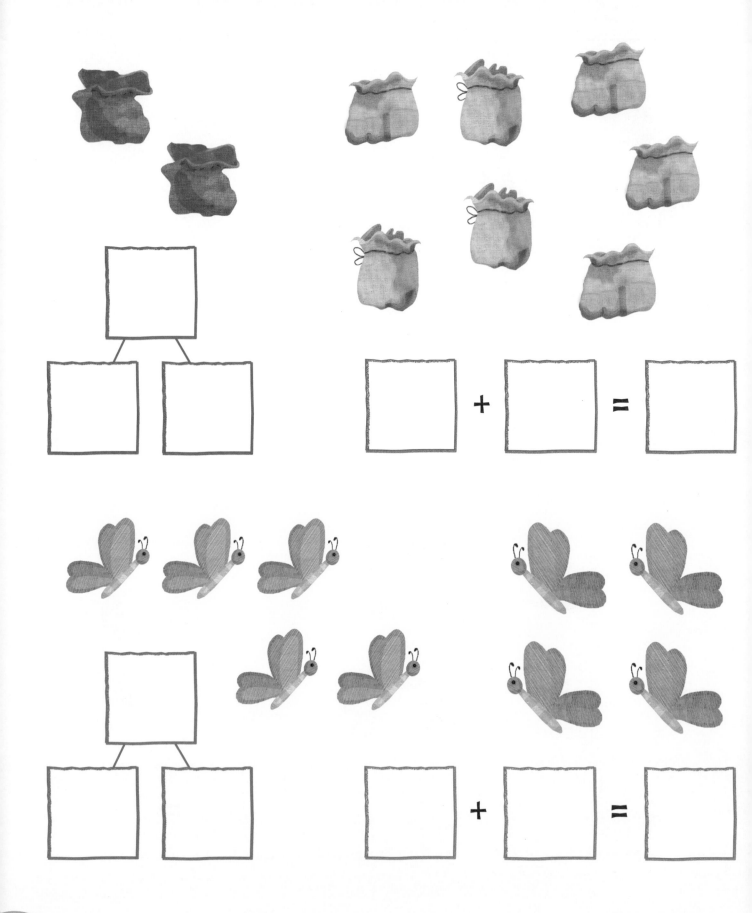

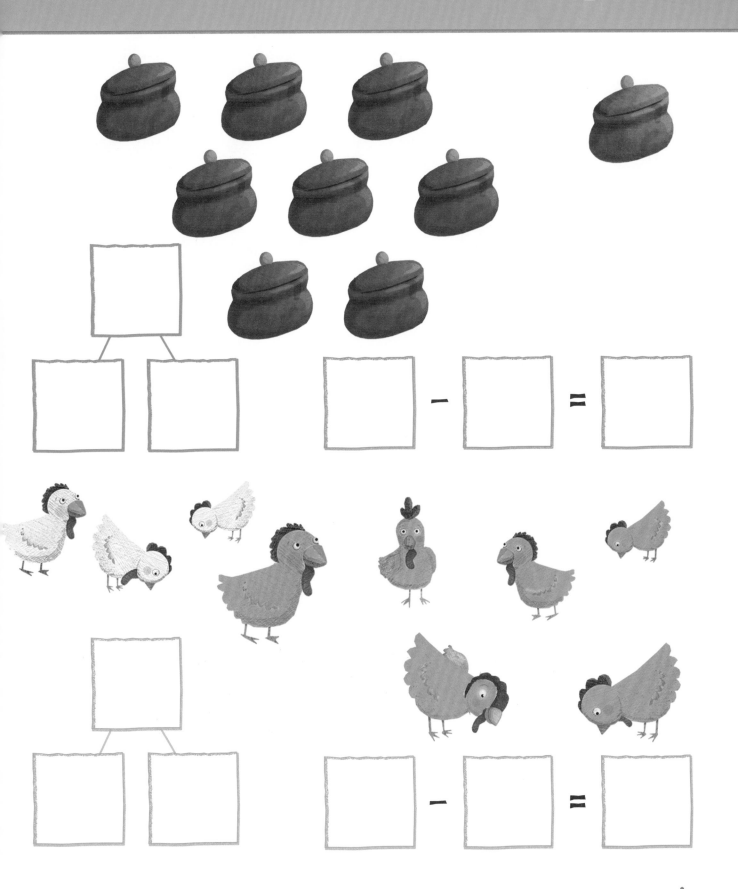

Well done!

Number facts for 10

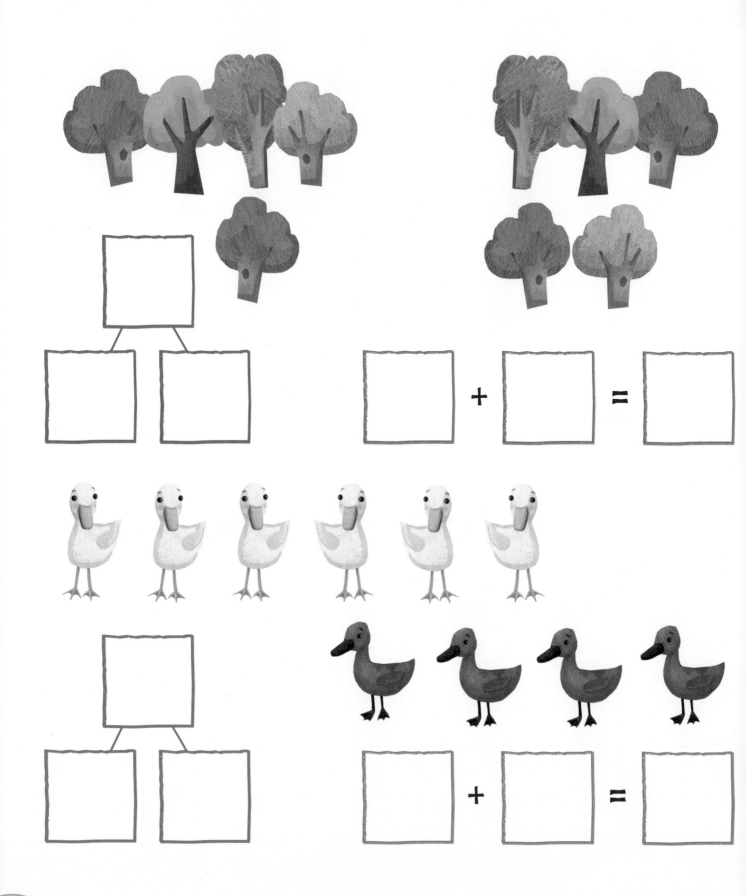

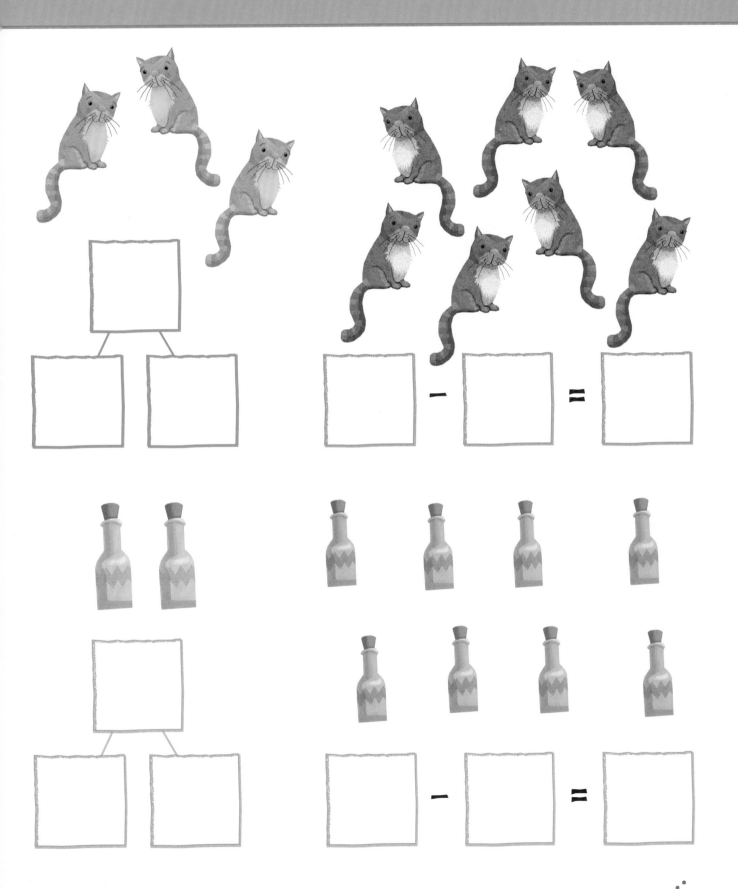

Well done!

More number facts for 10

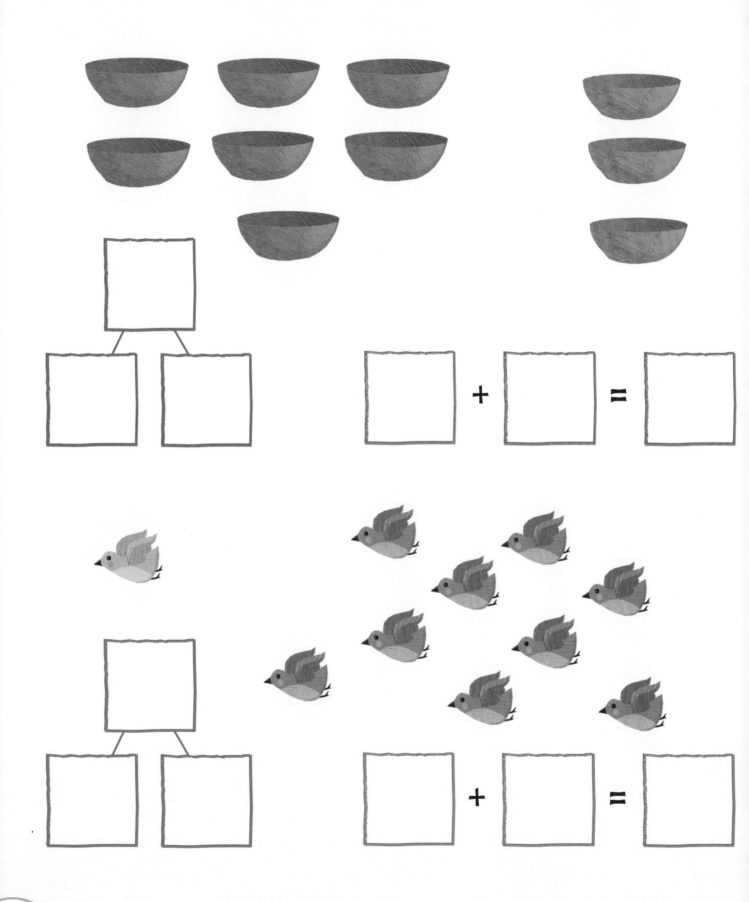

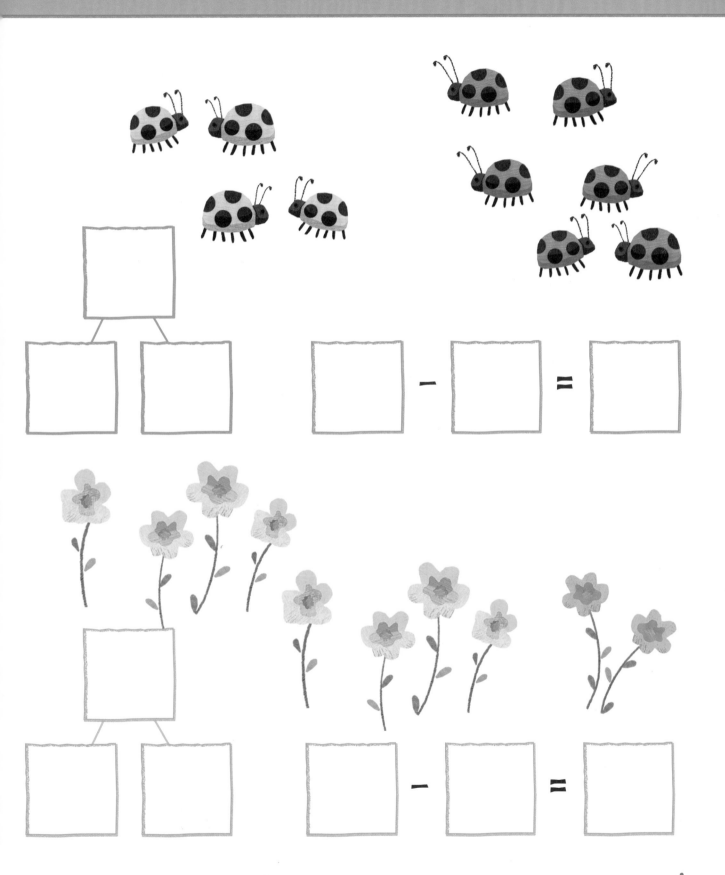

Well done!

WELL DONE!

You've finished
Number Skills

Write your name here

Now you know how to do lots of calculations with the numbers 1–10.

Wow! You've been very buzzy – I mean, busy!